Written by Catherine Zoller
Pictures by Mr. Sketches

RHYME & REASON
R&R
SERIES

"GETTING THESE BOOKS IN PEOPLE'S HANDS SO PEOPLE'S HANDS PICK UP THE BOOK."

ABOUT THE AUTHOR

Catherine Zoller is a writer from Tulsa, Oklahoma,
With a husband, three kids, and half a college diploma.

Many years ago the Lord spoke to her one night,
He said simply and clearly, "I want you to write!"

So she jumped out of bed and grabbed paper and a pen,
And waited on the sofa for Him to speak to her again.

At last there came the dawn with the dew and heavy mist,
But all that she had written was half a grocery list.

She never had forgotten all the words she heard that night;
All she had to learn was that His timing's always right.

And so she's written rhymes that tell the Bible story,
From Genesis to Revelation, to reveal God's glory.

The hope within her heart is to show everyone
That reading God's true Word can be a lot of fun!

It will instruct and teach you, and it can change your heart,
And this little book you hold is designed to help you start!

Exodus: The Rhyme and Reason Series by Catherine Zoller
Copyright ©2012 by Catherine Zoller
Printed in Canada

ISBN 978-0-9885122-0-7
For worldwide distribution

Rhyme & Reason Ministries International • P.O. Box 470994 • Tulsa, OK 74147-0994
You can learn more about Catherine Zoller at www.catherinezoller.com

ABOUT THE ILLUSTRATOR

The artist Mr. Sketches is also known by some
As Mr. David Wilson, and he thinks art is fun!

The nickname Mr. Sketches came from a T.V. show
The station TBN broadcast for three years in a row.

His lovely wife named Karen likes to teach the second grade.
They moved around a bit, but when they got to Tulsa stayed.

Art from the heart it surely helps God's children to succeed,
So when he draws and sketches, this is always David's creed:

"With broad point or with fine or whatever time or season,
It's time to draw the line now, whatever rhyme or reason!"

DEDICATION

This book is dedicated to young children everywhere.
May you always learn to trust in God's comfort and His care.

For surely as Queen Esther came, "For such time as this."
There's something only you can do or things will be amiss.

I pray that you will call on Him to show you your life's plan,
And walk with Him all of your days safely hand in hand.

3

The funny word "exodus" means simply "to go out."
Like when the Hebrew Nation went from Egypt with a shout.

It's the second book in the Bible after Genesis,
God had Moses write things down so that nothing was amiss.

Ol' Mo was taught in all the wisdom of Egyptian ways,
He grew up in the Pharaoh's court and lived there many days.

One fateful day he took some matters into his own hand;
He killed an Egyptian guard and was forced to flee the land.

As God so often does, He turned bad things into good,
By sending Moses back to lead the Hebrews as he should.

God used Mo's education and his many years in exile
to prepare him for the job to lead His people for a while.

God then tells us of their journey into the Promised Land,
He shows us all that they went through so we will understand

That our journey through this busy life has lots of twists and turns,
But God is always with us and He helps us grow and learn.

God wrote down His sacred law, which were rules for living right,
He gave us these Commandments to be guidance for our lives.

He lights our path and guides our way in all the things we do,
The Lord provides the things we need and gives us wisdom, too.

The Lord desires that each of us will strive to be like Him
To live our life in love and joy instead of hate and sin.

Take a lesson, then, from Moses and give to God your flaws
For He can even use our faults to further His great cause.

So listen to this tale of how He set His People free,
The great miracles He did, and His plans for you and me.

Let's learn about God's holy ways and see His mighty power,
and understand He's here with us in each and every hour!

This is the true account
　　of the Hebrews' mass exodus,
How they all fled from Egypt,
　　but they didn't take a bus.

Joseph was their patriarch, who lived to ripe old age,
Enjoying all blessings of a wise and trusted sage.

He finally left this Earth and four hundred years went past.
And now we join the story where Genesis left off last.

Joseph's family went to Egypt, a famine to escape,
It then took generations for God's great plan to take shape.

God's chosen people thrived and had greatly multiplied,
Until their numbers filled the land, spreading far and wide.

This mighty band would soon be called the twelve Israeli tribes.
Their growing population gave Egyptian folks bad vibes.

A new man rose to Pharaoh after many generations
He too was getting wary of the Hebrew population.

This Pharaoh feared the Hebrews might want a country of their own,
That they would join with Egypt's enemies and try to seize the throne.

Genesis 50:22-26; Exodus 1:1-10

7

He made the Hebrews slaves
    under his absolute command,
And worked them day and night
    till they could barely stand.

Forced into manual labor,
    mixing mud with straw and sticks,
The Hebrews groaned and sweated
    as they made the Pharaoh's bricks.

Exodus 1:11-14

Pharaoh told their midwives,
    "Kill each boy who's less than two!"
But these women loved and feared the Lord,
    so this they would not do.

They kept on reproducing
    and their numbers just got stronger.
Finally Pharaoh said one day,
    "This can't go on much longer!

"Each Hebrew baby boy must now
    be cast into the Nile."
And so this horrid practice
    was upheld for quite a while.

Exodus 1:15-22

And then a certain Levite mother
    bore a baby son,
She sheltered him for three months,
    for he was a special one.

She wove a wicker basket-boat
    and covered it with tar.
She put him in the Nile;
    his sister followed from afar.

Exodus 2:1-4

10

Later Pharaoh's daughter
    went to the river for a bath.
She found the crying baby boy
    and gave a little laugh.

His sister came and said she'd find
    a wet-nurse for the boy;
Then summoned his own mom to feed
    her little pride and joy.

The princess raised this baby boy
    as though he were her son,
and she named him "Moses,"
    for from the water he had come.

He grew up in the palace
    as a prince in Pharaoh's land
(Though later he would give it up
    to follow God's command).

Exodus 2:5-10   **11**

Many, many years went by and young Mo became a man.
One day he killed a wicked guard and covered him with sand.

The Egyptian had cruelly beaten one of Moses' own.
So Moses took his life and thought his deed was yet unknown.

Exodus 2:11-12 1:19-25

The next day when two Hebrew men got into a fight.
Moses said to both of them, "You know this isn't right."

One of them replied, "Who made *you* our judge today?
Are you going to kill me like that guy I saw you slay?"

Moses was so frightened
that to Midian he ran,
And hoped no one would find him
in that far and distant land.

Exodus 2:13-15

He met a priest with seven daughters
but without a son.
Moses helped the family out,
then wed the oldest one. *Exodus 2:16-21*

WEDDING
VOWS
I _____
Take _____
to be my lawful

14

Another forty years went past,
   the king of Egypt died.
But the Hebrews' fate grew worse,
   so out to God they cried.

Their pleas were heard by God
   who remembered the agreement
Made with Abraham and Isaac
   that was solid as cement.

Exodus 2:23-25

And then one day when Moses headed out to do his job,
He led his flock near Mount Horeb, and there he met with God!

Imagine his surprise to see a bush consumed in flame
And from within the burning bush a voice called out his name.

When Moses got up closer to see what he had found
God said, "Stop! Remove your shoes—you stand on holy ground."

He said, "My son, I've chosen you to set My people free
From their oppressive bondage 'cause I've heard their woeful plea."

"I'll lead you to a land that flows
    with milk and golden honey.
Then give it to My people;
    it can't be bought with money."

But Moses said to God,
    "Lord, I'm old and slow and weak;
There must be someone better—
    I'm not the man you seek."

God replied, "Don't worry son,
    'cause I'll always be with you.
So listen and I'll tell you now
    exactly what to do."

But Moses interrupted,
    asking, "What then shall I say?
And whom shall I tell the people
    will lead us on our way?"

16   *Exodus 3:1-13*

God then spoke to Moses, "Tell them 'I AM WHO I AM
The true God of your forefathers!' tell each woman and man.'

I'm Elohim, the Mighty God, the ever-present One
Deliverer, Redeemer, who will send My Savior Son.'

But poor Moses was still quaking and trembling with fear
He asked the Lord, "What if they don't believe the things they hear?'

"I will perform great miracles," the Living God replied
"They will see and then believe, and then gather by your side

"But Pharaoh—well, My friend, that'll be another story
He'll refuse to let My people go till everything gets gory

"It's My mighty power that will finally force his hand
Then I'll lead My people from Egypt into the Promised Land.'

But Moses quickly stammered
"Lord, I'm sure you don't want me
I've never spoken well
so it's a problem, don't You see?'

God was getting angry but said
"Then here is what you'll do
Go get your brother, Aaron
and I'll have him speak for you.'

So Mo returned to Egypt
with his staff held in his hand
Performing signs and wonders
for the Hebrews in the land

Exodus 3:1-1.

The miracles they saw
    left the people stunned and awed;
They all bowed down in worship
    to the true and living God.

Then Moses and his brother went
    to see Pharaoh the king,
To ask him for time off so they
    could worship God and sing.

But angry Pharaoh shouted, "No!"
    just as the Lord had said.
He worked the Hebrews harder then
    til they were nearly dead.

*Exodus 4:19-21;
4:28-31; 5:1-19*

Moses turned to God and asked,
  "Lord, were You merely bluffing?
Your people are still suffering
  but so far You've done nothing!"

But God answered, "Tell My people
  that they will soon be free,
Then I'll punish the Egyptians
  quite terribly, you'll see.

"The Hebrews are My chosen ones;
  I am their loving Lord.
Now go and tell ol' Pharaoh
  to let you leave in one accord.

"I know that he won't listen,
  so I promise I'll perform
fearful signs and wonders that
  will force him to conform."

Exodus 5:22-6:9

19

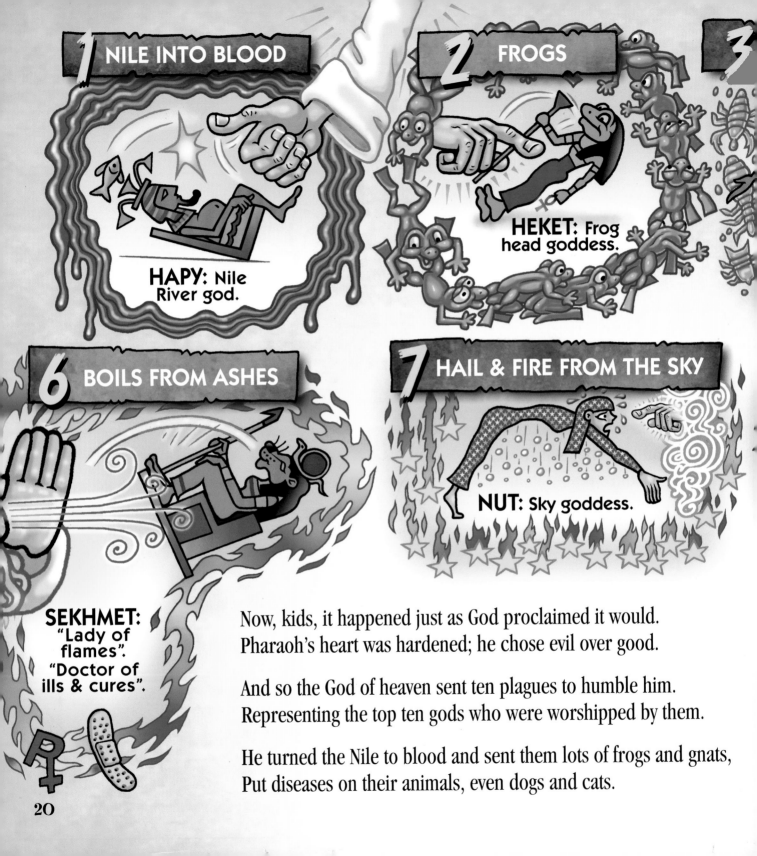

1 NILE INTO BLOOD

HAPY: Nile River god.

2 FROGS

HEKET: Frog head goddess.

3

6 BOILS FROM ASHES

SEKHMET: "Lady of flames". "Doctor of ills & cures".

7 HAIL & FIRE FROM THE SKY

NUT: Sky goddess.

Now, kids, it happened just as God proclaimed it would.
Pharaoh's heart was hardened; he chose evil over good.

And so the God of heaven sent ten plagues to humble him.
Representing the top ten gods who were worshipped by them.

He turned the Nile to blood and sent them lots of frogs and gnats,
Put diseases on their animals, even dogs and cats.

ICE FROM DUST

GEB: Earth soil god.

4 FLIES (INSECTS)

KHEPR: Dung beatle god.

5 CATTLE DIE

HATHOR: Cow goddess.

8 LOCUST EAT GRAIN

NEPRI: Grain god.

9 DARKNESS (FOR 3 DAYS)

CLAP CLAP

RA: Sun god.

Next came boils, then hail and fire,
    and insects, and then locusts.
The sun was blotted out,
    but it wasn't hocus pocus.

But the final plague of all
    was the most destructive one.
God's Angel went throughout the land
    to kill each first-born son.

Exodus 7:14-11:10

10 DEATH OF FIRST BORN

(lamb of god)
KHNUM: "Baa of Ra". Creator of human children on a potter's wheel. Head of RAM vs. Passover LAMB.

21

The Hebrews avoided this when they sacrificed a lamb,
Then smeared its blood as God commanded on the house door jamb.

They ate the lamb with bitter herbs and bread without the yeast.
God said, "Each year, remember the Passover with this feast."

Exodus 12:1-28

Meanwhile, all Egypt was wailing in suffering and pain.
Pharaoh said to Moses, "You won't have to ask again.

"Take your children and your cattle and your donkeys and your sheep,
Go far away and worship at your Lord God's feet."

Exodus 12:29-32

So all the Hebrews packed with haste and left their homes with glee.
They hurried through the desert heading toward the great Red Sea.

With a mighty pillar of cloud, God guided them by day.
At night it turned to blazing fire to lead them on their way.

Exodus 12:34-36; 13:21-22

24

After they had left, though, Pharaoh changed his wicked mind
He needed all the slaves back to perform their daily grind.

He took six hundred chariots and out his army came
To recapture the poor Hebrews so their lives would be the same.

Exodus 14:5-9

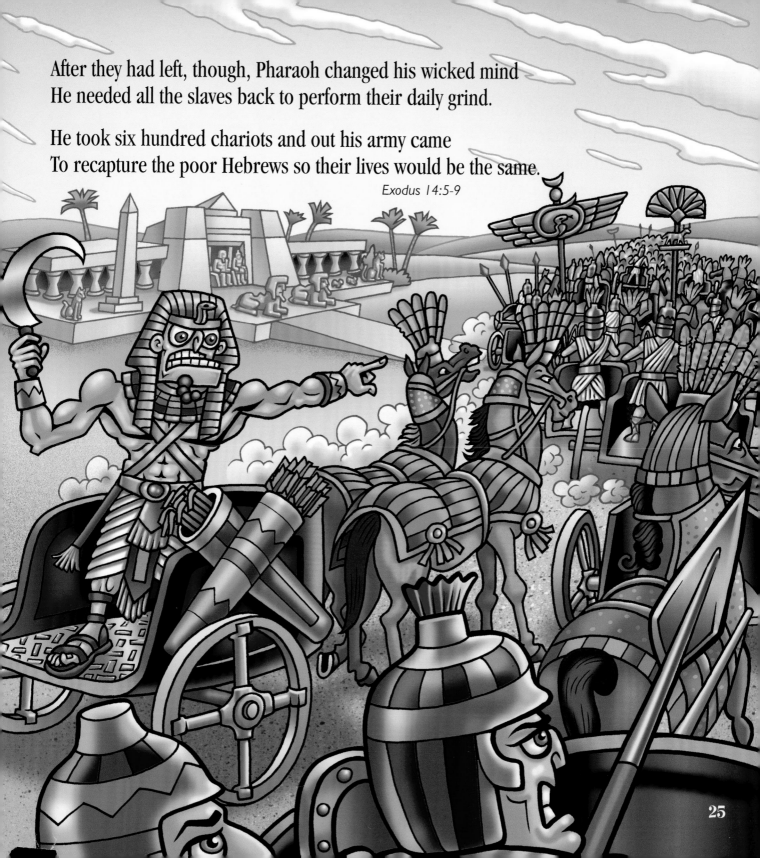

25

When people saw the mighty army
    hastening their way,
They cried out unto Moses,
    "Oh, why didn't we just stay?

"We could have stayed in Egypt
    and not come out here to die!"
But Moses said, "Be patient,
    there's no need to wail and cry."

Exodus 14:10-14

A great cloud made a barrier between the camps all night.
The Egyptians dwelt in darkness, but the Hebrews had bright light.

Exodus 14:19-20

Moses stood and stretched his staff out o'er the wide Red Sea.
A strong wind blew in from the east—the waters did recede.

Exodus 14:21

28

The Hebrews crossed on dry land 'tween the massive walls of sea
Held there by God's mighty hand so His people could go free!

Exodus 14:22

29

But the army's passage through the water didn't go so well.
When Moses raised his staff again, the walls of water fell.

Then all the horses and the chariots hot upon their trail
Were swallowed by the sea; again the Lord prevailed.

So when the Hebrew people saw the wonders God had done,
They finally recognized that Moses was God's chosen one.

Exodus 14:23-28

Safely on the other side,
    they began to dance about,
Singing songs that celebrated
    how God had brought them out!

They lifted up the name of God
    who had triumphed gloriously;
From their former masters,
    He had finally set them free.

Exodus 15:1-21

Now kids, I hate to tell you,
    but it wasn't very long
'Til grumbling and complaining stole
    their joy and changed their song.

Three days later, they found the water
    too bitter to drink,
Then grumbled to poor Moses, saying,
    "What are we to think?

Did God bring us from Egypt
    to the desert so we'd die?"
Moses raised his voice in prayer
    and asked the Lord God, "Why?"

Exodus 15:22-24

The Lord came to the rescue and showed Moses a tree,
He threw it in the waters and the waters became sweet.

The waters poured forth and they flowed out ever wider,
For He's *Jehovah-Jireh*, our Father and Provider.

Then God said to the people, "If you'll listen to My voice,
And you keep all My commandments and make the proper choice,

"Then none of the diseases from Egypt will affect you
Jehovah-Rapha heals them all, and not only a few."

Exodus 15:25-26

But It wasn't too long before the grumbling began.
"There is nothing here to eat, and we've no food in our hand.

"At least back in Egypt we had plenty of food to eat.
God has brought us to the desert to die amid the heat."

Moses said to them,
    "God has heard what you have spoken,
Now each day when you wake,
    you'll have fresh bread to be broken.

"Then you all will see just how much
    your Lord God cares for you
As you gather your daily manna
    in the morning dew.

"But please listen to me now,
    and my words you must obey.
Don't gather any more than you
    can eat in just one day." *Exodus 16:1-18*

ARK
COVENANT
PARK

34

Some people disobeyed the Lord and set more bread aside,
But overnight worms were sent to make it putrified!

The day before the Sabbath they were told to gather more
Because it was a holy day, two days worth they could store.

Soon there came another day
   they couldn't find fresh waters.
They whined to Mo, "We'll die here
   with all our sons and daughters!"

Moses beseeched the God of Heaven
   and of Earth below,
Then smacked a rock on Mount Horeb
   to make the water flow.

Despite the wondrous works and all
   that God had done for them,
The people's hearts were stubborn
   and they wouldn't trust in Him.

Exodus 16:19-21; 17:1-6

35

About this time Amalekites came out to start a fight.
They came against the Hebrews will their power and their might.

So Moses asked brave Joshua to gather up some men.
Because he knew that with God's help, this battle they would win.

Exodus 17:8-11

When Moses held his arms up, the battle went their way,
But he couldn't keep on doing that all throughout the day.

When his arms tired out and he could no longer stand,
He sat down on a rock while Hur and Aaron lent a hand.

They held his arms up all that day until the sun went down.
The Hebrews won the battle and the story passed around.

So then Moses built an altar
   to *Jehovah-Nissi*,
Which means, "The Lord's my banner—
   He will protect and keep me."

Exodus 17:12-16

"**O**n eagles' wings I've carried them through years of slavery.
A new land I'll provide where they can love and worship Me.

"They will be My people, a holy nation led by priests,
Set apart as Chosen Ones from the greatest to the least."

The people then responded, "What He's spoken, we will do!"
God told them, "Get ready, because I'm coming down to you."

He came with peals of thunder
   and flashes of bright lightening.
His presence was so awesome
   and truly was quite frightening.

The entire mountain quaked
   and was covered in thick smoke.
The trumpets blasted louder
   as God and Moses spoke.

One thing God insisted on,
   the one thing that was vital:
He is very much *alive*
   and not dead like an idol.

God then spoke to Moses, saying,
   "Climb up on Mount Sinai."
He gave Mo the ten commandments
   His people to live by:

Exodus 19:3-25

Rev. 18:1-19:2

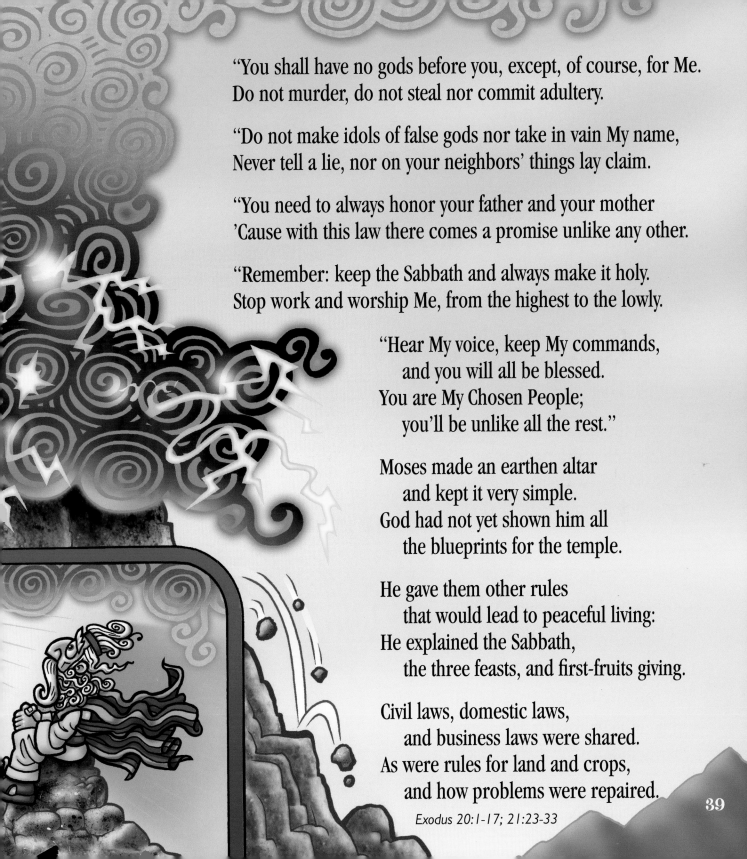

"You shall have no gods before you, except, of course, for Me.
Do not murder, do not steal nor commit adultery.

"Do not make idols of false gods nor take in vain My name,
Never tell a lie, nor on your neighbors' things lay claim.

"You need to always honor your father and your mother
'Cause with this law there comes a promise unlike any other.

"Remember: keep the Sabbath and always make it holy.
Stop work and worship Me, from the highest to the lowly.

"Hear My voice, keep My commands,
    and you will all be blessed.
You are My Chosen People;
    you'll be unlike all the rest."

Moses made an earthen altar
    and kept it very simple.
God had not yet shown him all
    the blueprints for the temple.

He gave them other rules
    that would lead to peaceful living:
He explained the Sabbath,
    the three feasts, and first-fruits giving.

Civil laws, domestic laws,
    and business laws were shared.
As were rules for land and crops,
    and how problems were repaired.

Exodus 20:1-17; 21:23-33

39

But the turbulence and noise
    made the people shake in fear.
They were terrified of God,
    and they did not want Him near.

So the people said to Moses,
    "Feel free to be our guy.
If God Himself should speak to us,
    then surely we will die!

"You just tell us what He says
    when you hear from up above."
They only saw His fearful strength
    and not His tender love.

Yet when they saw His miracles,
    the people were quite awed.
But even these were not enough
    to make them love their God.

Because they were afraid,
    they began to fret and yell.
So God gave Mo the plans to build
    a place where He could dwell.

God recognized their fear,
    so He kindly gave them distance.
And had the words He'd spoken
    written down for their assistance.

Exodus 20:18-21

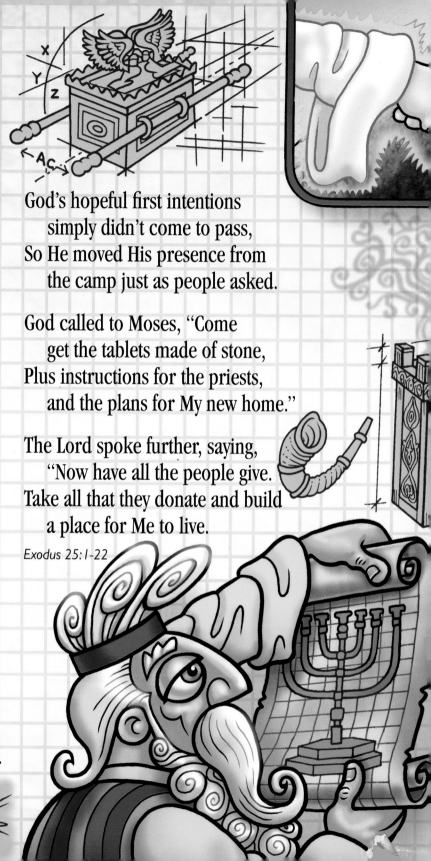

God's hopeful first intentions
    simply didn't come to pass,
So He moved His presence from
    the camp just as people asked.

God called to Moses, "Come
    get the tablets made of stone,
Plus instructions for the priests,
    and the plans for My new home."

The Lord spoke further, saying,
    "Now have all the people give.
Take all that they donate and build
    a place for Me to live.

Exodus 25:1-22

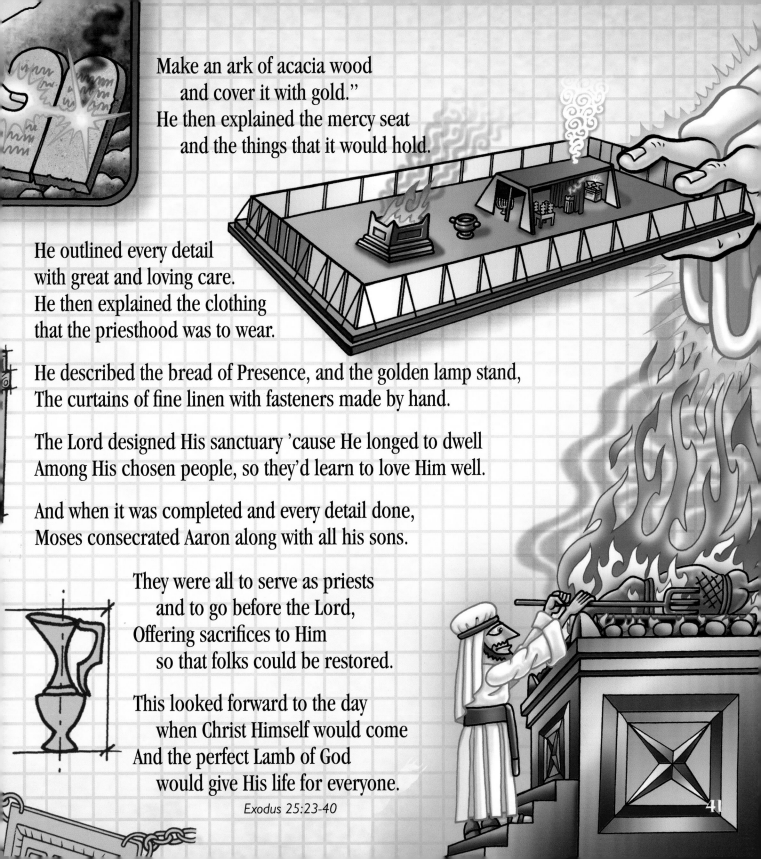

Make an ark of acacia wood
    and cover it with gold."
He then explained the mercy seat
    and the things that it would hold.

He outlined every detail
with great and loving care.
He then explained the clothing
that the priesthood was to wear.

He described the bread of Presence, and the golden lamp stand,
The curtains of fine linen with fasteners made by hand.

The Lord designed His sanctuary 'cause He longed to dwell
Among His chosen people, so they'd learn to love Him well.

And when it was completed and every detail done,
Moses consecrated Aaron along with all his sons.

They were all to serve as priests
    and to go before the Lord,
Offering sacrifices to Him
    so that folks could be restored.

This looked forward to the day
    when Christ Himself would come
And the perfect Lamb of God
    would give His life for everyone.

Exodus 25:23-40

41

Mo was gone forty days
    to get commandments from the Lord,
But the people down below
    were getting fidgety and bored.

So they said to Aaron,
    "Make us a god we can behold!"
He melted down their jewelry
    to make a calf of gold.

Now can't you just imagine how they danced around this calf?
It all seems very silly, and it makes you want to laugh!

But I am here to tell you that throughout our history
We have all created idols, including you and me.

Exodus 24:18; 32:1-6

42

Anything we care about and worship more than God above
Can lure and make us turn away from God's redeeming love.

And so these stubborn people, how quickly they forgot
All that God had done for them; the freedom He had brought.

The Lord was angry, said, "Moses, go down to your people.
They made a golden idol and are doing what is evil.

"Leave Me here alone, full of righteous indignation!
I'll destroy these people and make of you a greater nation."

Moses prayed to God and said, "But what will Egypt say?
That You brought us to the desert just to wipe us all away!

You made a great big promise to Abraham and Israel
That You'd increase their descendents and now that plan will fail."

Exodus 32:7-13

Moses' plea had changed God's mind,
   and so Mo started down.
But when he reached the camp and saw
   the calf they danced around,

His anger turned to fury
   at the party that he found.
He threw the tablets from his hands;
   they shattered on the ground.

Now, no one likes to think
   that brother Aaron was a liar,
But he claimed when he threw in gold,
   the calf jumped from the fire!

So the judgment of our God
   came quickly down upon them
To address their rebellion
   and cleanse them of their sin.

Moses prayed again and for
   the people, he repented.
He cried out on behalf of them
   and then the Lord relented.

God said to Moses, "Servant,
   you've found favor in My sight,"
And He promised once again
   they'd have the land of all the 'ites.'

Exodus 32:14-33

"I will send an angel who will walk the trail before you."
But Moses shook his head and said, "That simply will not do.

"If You do not go with us, will not lead us there from here,
Then I and all your people will take every step in fear.

"Only You can keep us safe
    and give us promised rest.
We need You with us now
    and whenever we're distressed."

After all his time before the Lord,
    Moses' face had brightened.
He had to wear a veil
    so the people were not frightened.

God made a promise to His people:
    they would beat all odds
if they crossed into the Promised Land
    but rejected other gods.

Once more He wrote on tablets
    He had Moses make from stone,
Commandments for the people that
    He called His very own.

Exodus 32:34-34:5

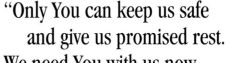

45

They all got very busy and
     they built the tabernacle.
Working all together,
     it was not too big to tackle.

Because they were committed and
     they worked and worked each day,
They completed all the work required
     in God's specific way.

Ol' Mo examined all the work
     that all of them had done,
And then invoked a blessing
     on each and every one.

The tabernacle was erected
     just outside the camp.
God's presence hovered over it
     like a radiant lamp.

Throughout their journey God
     dwelled over the tent of meeting.
In a mighty cloud by day,
     and with fire in the evening.

Exodus 35:21-40:38

Let us each take a lesson now from all that we have read,
And learn to listen to the Lord so we are Spirit led.

Choose to walk with Him
   and let Him guide you on your way,
Because the Lord Almighty
   loves you more than words can say!

He knows what's best for each of us
   and what our lives can render.
The lives we live begin again
   the moment we surrender.

As Moses went from serving God
   to being His good friend,
Let each of us make that choice
   our chief goal and our end!